Carbon Markets

Diego Hidalgo-Oñate

DIEGO HIDALGO-OÑATE

CARBON
MARKETS

TABLE OF CONTENTS

Chapter 1: Forests as Carbon Sinks and Climate Change Mitigators

Forests play a pivotal role in the global carbon cycle, serving as significant carbon sinks and critical agents for mitigating climate change. This chapter explores the scientific underpinnings of forests' capacity to sequester carbon and contribute to climate change mitigation strategies.

Forest Carbon Sequestration Mechanisms: Forests capture and store carbon dioxide through the process of photosynthesis. Trees absorb atmospheric CO_2, converting it into biomass while releasing oxygen. This process, coupled with carbon storage in soils and woody materials, effectively removes carbon from the atmosphere.

Carbon Sequestration Rates Across Biomes: Different forest biomes exhibit varying rates of carbon sequestration due to factors such as species composition, growth rates, and environmental conditions. For instance, tropical forests sequester 4 to 7 tonnes of CO_2 per hectare per year, while temperate forests sequester 2 to 5 tonnes, and boreal forests sequester 1 to 3 tonnes.

The Role of Reforestation and Afforestation: Reforestation and afforestation initiatives are vital for enhancing carbon sequestration. Reforestation involves restoring forests on previously deforested land, while afforestation entails planting trees in areas that were not historically forested. These efforts contribute to carbon sequestration, habitat restoration, and biodiversity conservation.

Forest Management Practices: Sustainable forest management practices can optimize carbon sequestration. Thinning, which involves selectively removing trees, can enhance forest health and growth, while minimizing carbon loss through natural mortality.

Case Study: The Amazon Rainforest: The Amazon rainforest, often referred to as the "lungs of the Earth," is a critical carbon sink. Its vast biomass stores immense amounts of carbon, but deforestation threatens its capacity to sequester carbon. Efforts to curb deforestation and promote sustainable land use are essential for preserving this vital ecosystem.

Synergies Between Forest Conservation and Climate Goals: Forests offer co-benefits beyond carbon sequestration, including biodiversity preservation, watershed protection, and sustainable livelihoods. These co-benefits reinforce the importance of forest conservation in climate change mitigation.

Conclusion: The scientific evidence underscores the crucial role of forests in mitigating climate change by sequestering carbon. Reforestation, afforestation, and sustainable forest management are essential strategies for enhancing carbon sinks and contributing to global climate goals.

Chapter 2: The Emergence of the Carbon Market

Introduction: The Emergence of the Carbon Market

The modern carbon market has its roots in international efforts to combat climate change and reduce greenhouse gas emissions. It represents a significant shift in environmental policy, promoting market-based mechanisms to incentivize emission reductions and encourage sustainable practices. This chapter delves into the origins, mechanisms, and evolution of the carbon market, exploring its role in driving climate action and fostering a low-carbon economy.

The Kyoto Protocol and the Birth of Carbon Trading: The Kyoto Protocol, adopted in 1997 and implemented in 2005, marked a landmark international agreement aimed at reducing greenhouse gas emissions. It introduced the concept of carbon trading, allowing countries with emission reduction commitments to meet their targets by purchasing carbon credits from countries that exceeded their targets. This concept laid the foundation for the carbon market, creating a platform for the buying and selling of carbon credits as a way to achieve emission reduction goals.

Mechanisms of the Carbon Market: The carbon market operates through various mechanisms, each designed to facilitate emission reductions and promote sustainable practices:

1. **Cap-and-Trade Systems:** Cap-and-trade systems, also known as emissions trading systems (ETS), impose a limit (cap) on total allowable emissions and allocate allowances to participating entities. Entities that emit fewer emissions than their allowances can sell the surplus allowances to those exceeding their limits. The European Union Emissions Trading System (EU ETS) is one of the most prominent cap-and-trade systems globally.

2. **Clean Development Mechanism (CDM):** Established under the Kyoto Protocol, the CDM allows developed countries to invest in emission reduction projects in developing countries as a way to earn Certified Emission Reductions (CERs). These CERs can be used to meet part of the developed countries' emission reduction targets.

3. **Joint Implementation (JI):** Similar to the CDM, JI allows developed countries to invest in emission reduction projects in other developed countries to earn Emission Reduction Units (ERUs).

4. **Voluntary Carbon Market:** The voluntary carbon market allows businesses, individuals, and organizations to purchase carbon credits voluntarily to offset their emissions. This market has gained traction due to corporate sustainability initiatives and consumer demand for environmentally friendly products and services.

Evolution of the Carbon Market: The carbon market has witnessed significant growth and evolution since its inception. The value of carbon trading has increased substantially, reflecting the market's expanding role in climate mitigation efforts. For instance, between 2005 and 2019, the global carbon market grew from $31 billion to $215 billion, with an average annual growth rate of approximately 15% (Source: World Bank).

Case Study: The European Union Emissions Trading System (EU ETS): One of the most prominent examples of a cap-and-trade system is the EU ETS, established in 2005. It covers various sectors, including energy, industry, and aviation, and has gone through multiple phases to enhance its effectiveness. The EU ETS has played a pivotal role in reducing emissions within the European Union while fostering technological innovation and sustainable practices.

Conclusion: The emergence of the carbon market reflects a transformative approach to addressing climate change. By creating economic incentives for emission reductions and sustainable practices, the market leverages market forces to advance climate goals. As the global community continues to prioritize environmental stewardship, the carbon market's evolution remains integral to achieving a low-carbon future.

Chapter 3: Reforestation and Carbon Sequestration

This chapter delves into the scientific foundations of reforestation as a vital strategy for carbon sequestration, exploring the mechanisms, benefits, and challenges of restoring forests to mitigate climate change.

The Role of Reforestation in Carbon Sequestration: Reforestation is a natural climate solution that involves restoring forests on degraded or deforested lands. Trees capture atmospheric carbon dioxide through photosynthesis, storing carbon in their biomass, roots, and soil.

Carbon Sequestration Mechanisms: Reforestation contributes to carbon sequestration through multiple mechanisms. As trees grow, they absorb carbon dioxide and convert it into organic matter. Soil organic carbon increases as fallen leaves, branches, and decomposed material enrich the forest floor.

Potential for Carbon Removal: Forests have immense potential to remove carbon dioxide from the atmosphere. Different forest types exhibit varying carbon sequestration rates. Tropical forests sequester more carbon due to their high productivity and rapid growth rates.

Biodiversity and Ecosystem Services: Reforestation contributes to biodiversity conservation and provides essential ecosystem services. Forests offer habitats for diverse species, support pollination, regulate water cycles, and prevent soil erosion.

Challenges and Risks: Reforestation projects face challenges such as selecting appropriate tree species, ensuring sustainable management, and addressing potential trade-offs with other land uses. Invasive species and inadequate monitoring can also hinder project success.

Case Study: A Successful Reforestation Project: The Bonn Challenge, a global initiative, aims to restore 350 million hectares of deforested and degraded land by 2030. The "20x20" initiative in Latin America and the Caribbean exemplifies successful reforestation efforts.

Scaling Up Reforestation: Scaling up reforestation requires addressing barriers and mobilizing resources. Financial incentives, technical expertise, and community engagement play critical roles in expanding reforestation initiatives.

Carbon Offsetting and Reforestation: Reforestation projects generate carbon offsets that can be sold in carbon markets. These offsets enable industries to compensate for their emissions by investing in forest restoration.

The Future of Reforestation: Incorporating reforestation into climate policy is essential to achieve carbon neutrality goals. Collaborative efforts between governments, NGOs, and businesses can drive ambitious reforestation targets.

Conclusion: Reforestation stands as a scientifically supported strategy for carbon sequestration, with the potential to mitigate climate change, enhance biodiversity, and provide vital ecosystem services. As the world grapples with climate challenges, reforestation offers a nature-based solution for a sustainable future.

Chapter 4: Carbon Sequestration in Forest Ecosystems

This chapter delves into the intricate science behind carbon sequestration in forest ecosystems, exploring the vital role that trees and forests play in absorbing atmospheric carbon dioxide. It examines the processes, mechanisms, and factors influencing carbon capture, highlighting the potential of afforestation, reforestation, and sustainable forest management in mitigating climate change.

The Role of Trees in Carbon Sequestration: Trees are nature's carbon capture and storage units. Through photosynthesis, trees absorb carbon dioxide from the atmosphere and convert it into biomass – a process that helps mitigate the greenhouse effect. Carbon is stored in various components of trees, including leaves, stems, branches, and roots, as well as in forest soils.

Processes of Carbon Sequestration: Carbon sequestration involves intricate biological and physical processes. As trees grow, they accumulate biomass, acting as carbon sinks. When leaves fall and organic matter decomposes, carbon is incorporated into the soil. Furthermore, mycorrhizal fungi form symbiotic relationships with tree roots, enhancing nutrient and carbon exchange between trees and soils.

Influence of Forest Management: Sustainable forest management practices significantly impact carbon sequestration. Thinning, for instance, can enhance tree growth and carbon storage by reducing competition for resources. Conversely, logging and deforestation release stored carbon back into the atmosphere, underscoring the importance of preserving existing forests.

Climate, Species, and Soil Interactions: The interaction between climate, tree species, and soil types shapes carbon sequestration potential. Tropical forests, with their high species diversity and rapid growth, exhibit substantial sequestration rates. Temperate and boreal forests, while sequestering less carbon per unit area, cover vast expanses and contribute significantly to global carbon storage.

Case Study: The Role of Mangroves in Carbon Sequestration: Mangroves, coastal ecosystems dominated by salt-tolerant trees, are exceptional carbon sinks. Their intricate root systems trap organic matter, fostering sediment accumulation and carbon storage. Mangroves sequester carbon at rates higher than many other ecosystems, making them essential allies in climate change mitigation.

Conclusion: The science of carbon sequestration in forest ecosystems unveils nature's ingenious capacity to mitigate climate change. As we unravel the mechanisms that drive carbon capture and storage in trees, forests emerge as critical allies in the battle against rising carbon dioxide levels. Sustainable forest management, afforestation, and reforestation stand as powerful tools to harness the potential of carbon sequestration and foster a sustainable future.

Chapter 5: Carbon Markets and Trading Mechanisms

This chapter delves into the scientific and economic foundations of carbon markets and trading mechanisms, illuminating the intricate web of transactions that underpins the global effort to mitigate climate change. It explores the development, functioning, and challenges of carbon markets, as well as the key players and strategies driving emissions reduction.

Economics of Carbon Pricing: Carbon pricing is rooted in economic theory that aims to internalize the external costs of carbon emissions. By assigning a monetary value to carbon, carbon pricing mechanisms incentivize emissions reduction. Two main types of carbon pricing mechanisms are carbon taxes and emissions trading systems (ETS).

Evolution of Carbon Markets: Carbon markets have evolved over decades, from the Clean Air Act in the United States to the Kyoto Protocol's Clean Development Mechanism (CDM) and the Paris Agreement's market mechanisms. The European Union Emissions Trading System (EU ETS) is the world's largest carbon market, fostering emissions reduction across industries.

Emissions Trading Systems (ETS): ETS are central to carbon trading. They cap emissions and allow the trading of emission allowances among participants. The cap ensures emissions reduction targets are met, while trading allows flexibility for industries to innovate and reduce emissions cost-effectively.

Case Study: The European Union Emissions Trading System (EU ETS): The EU ETS, established in 2005, covers sectors like power generation, aviation, and heavy industry. Its phased approach and allocation methodologies have evolved over time. Despite challenges, the EU ETS has shown that market-based mechanisms can drive emissions reductions.

Offsets and Carbon Projects: Offsets, generated through emissions reduction projects, play a crucial role in carbon markets. Projects like reforestation, renewable energy, and methane capture generate offsets, which can be traded or used to comply with emissions targets.

The Role of Financial Instruments: Carbon markets rely on financial instruments like carbon credits and allowances. These instruments represent emissions reductions or the right to emit a certain amount of carbon. Financial players, including banks, investment funds, and carbon brokers, facilitate market transactions.

Challenges and Future Prospects: Carbon markets face challenges, including ensuring environmental integrity, preventing market manipulation, and addressing concerns of social equity. The transition to a global carbon market, as envisioned in the Paris Agreement's Article 6, holds promise for further emissions reduction.

Conclusion: Carbon markets and trading mechanisms represent a dynamic landscape where science and economics converge to combat climate change. By placing a price on carbon, these mechanisms incentivize emissions reduction, drive innovation, and pave the way for a low-carbon future. Their continued evolution, guided by scientific insights and economic principles, offers a path toward a more sustainable world.

Chapter 6: The Emergence of Carbon Offset Projects and REDD+

This chapter explores the scientific underpinnings of carbon offset projects, with a focus on the REDD+ framework (Reducing Emissions from Deforestation and Forest Degradation), which seeks to address deforestation and promote sustainable forest management.

Deforestation and Climate Impact: Deforestation contributes significantly to greenhouse gas emissions, as trees absorb carbon dioxide during photosynthesis. The loss of forests disrupts the carbon cycle, releasing stored carbon into the atmosphere and exacerbating climate change.

REDD+ Framework: REDD+ is a mechanism established under the United Nations Framework Convention on Climate Change (UNFCCC) to incentivize developing countries to reduce deforestation and promote sustainable forest management. It encompasses five pillars: reducing emissions from deforestation, reducing emissions from forest degradation, conservation of forest carbon stocks, sustainable management of forests, and enhancement of forest carbon stocks.

Scientific Assessments and Measurement: Accurate measurement and monitoring of carbon stocks and emissions in forests are essential for implementing effective

REDD+ projects. Remote sensing technologies, such as satellite imagery and LiDAR, provide valuable data for assessing forest cover, biomass, and changes over time.

Case Study: The Mai Ndombe REDD+ Project (Democratic Republic of Congo): The Mai Ndombe project demonstrates how REDD+ can contribute to emission reductions, biodiversity conservation, and community development. By engaging local communities, implementing sustainable land-use practices, and protecting intact forests, the project illustrates the potential for multiple co-benefits.

Safeguards and Social Considerations: REDD+ projects must adhere to safeguards that protect the rights of indigenous peoples and local communities and avoid negative social and environmental impacts. The Free, Prior, and Informed Consent (FPIC) principle ensures community participation and consent in project design and implementation.

Financing REDD+ Projects: Financial mechanisms, including public and private funding, contribute to the success of REDD+ projects. Initiatives like the Green Climate Fund (GCF) provide financial support for developing countries to implement REDD+ activities.

Challenges and Future Prospects: REDD+ faces challenges, such as ensuring equitable benefit-sharing, addressing leakage (shifting deforestation to other areas), and establishing robust monitoring and verification systems. As nations strive to enhance their Nationally Determined Contributions

(NDCs) under the Paris Agreement, REDD+ holds potential to contribute to ambitious emission reduction targets.

Conclusion: Carbon offset projects, particularly those under the REDD+ framework, play a pivotal role in mitigating climate change by curbing deforestation and promoting sustainable forest management. Scientific advancements in monitoring and measurement, coupled with social safeguards and financial support, are essential for the success of such projects, contributing to a more resilient and sustainable future.

Chapter 7: The Carbon Market and Market Mechanisms

This chapter delves into the scientific foundations of the carbon market and various market mechanisms designed to reduce greenhouse gas emissions and promote sustainable practices.

Carbon Market and Emission Trading: The carbon market is a market-based approach to mitigate climate change by putting a price on carbon emissions. Emission trading allows companies with lower emissions to sell excess allowances to those exceeding their limits. This incentivizes emission reductions where they can be achieved most efficiently.

Economic Theory and Efficiency: Market mechanisms are rooted in economic theory, particularly the Coase Theorem, which suggests that when property rights are well-defined, parties can negotiate optimal solutions to externalities, like pollution, through voluntary transactions. Carbon pricing aligns with this principle, internalizing the social cost of carbon.

Cap and Trade vs. Carbon Tax: Two primary market mechanisms are cap and trade and carbon tax. Cap and trade sets a cap on total emissions and allows trading of emission allowances. Carbon tax directly taxes emissions, encouraging companies to reduce emissions to minimize costs.

Case Study: European Union Emissions Trading System (EU ETS): The EU ETS, the world's largest carbon market, showcases the application of cap and trade. Its phases have seen evolution, successes, and challenges, providing insights into the complexities of implementing a market-based approach.

Innovation and Technological Transition: Carbon pricing encourages innovation in low-carbon technologies. The market rewards companies that adopt cleaner practices and invest in research and development of emission-reduction solutions.

Price Volatility and Risk Management: Carbon markets can experience price volatility, affecting the stability of emission reduction efforts. Financial instruments, such as carbon futures and options, provide risk management tools for market participants.

Linking Carbon Markets: Interconnected carbon markets allow for greater flexibility and increased efficiency. Linkage harmonizes carbon prices across jurisdictions, creating a larger, more liquid market.

Carbon Offsetting and Sustainable Finance: Carbon offset projects generate offset credits that can be used by companies to meet their emission reduction targets. Sustainable finance integrates carbon offsets as a tool to align financial decisions with environmental goals.

Challenges and Future Prospects: Market mechanisms face challenges, including ensuring environmental integrity, avoiding market manipulation, and addressing equity concerns. The expansion of carbon markets and integration with other policy instruments offer prospects for enhanced climate action.

Conclusion: Market mechanisms harness economic principles to address climate change by assigning a value to carbon emissions. Through carbon pricing and trading, these mechanisms incentivize emission reductions, promote innovation, and drive the transition to a sustainable, low-carbon economy.

Chapter 8: Carbon Credits and Project-Based Mechanisms

In this chapter, we delve into the scientific underpinnings of carbon credits and project-based mechanisms, exploring how these innovative approaches contribute to emissions reduction and sustainable development.

Carbon Credits and Offsetting: Carbon credits represent a quantified reduction of greenhouse gas emissions. Offsetting involves investing in projects that reduce or remove emissions to compensate for one's own emissions. This mechanism allows emissions to be balanced by equivalent emission reductions elsewhere.

Project-Based Mechanisms: Project-based mechanisms enable emission reductions to be achieved through specific projects, such as renewable energy installations, reforestation, or energy efficiency improvements. These mechanisms drive technology transfer, innovation, and sustainable development.

Additionality and Baselines: The concept of additionality ensures that emission reductions from projects would not have occurred without the incentive of carbon credits. Establishing accurate baselines is crucial to measuring the additionality of projects.

Case Study: Clean Development Mechanism (CDM): The CDM, established under the Kyoto Protocol, exemplifies project-based mechanisms. It allows developed countries to invest in emission reduction projects in developing countries and earn Certified Emission Reductions (CERs).

Co-Benefits and Sustainable Development: Many emission reduction projects yield co-benefits beyond carbon mitigation, such as improved air quality, job creation, and enhanced energy security. These co-benefits contribute to broader sustainable development goals.

Leakage and Permanence: Leakage refers to the unintended increase in emissions outside the project boundary due to market-driven shifts. Permanence addresses the risk of carbon stored in projects being released back into the atmosphere over time.

Safeguards and Certification: Certification standards ensure the quality and environmental integrity of carbon credit projects. These standards require rigorous monitoring, reporting, and verification to ensure real emission reductions.

Scaling Up and Sectoral Approaches: Scaling up project-based mechanisms requires aligning with sectoral approaches that target entire industries. Sectoral mechanisms offer potential for greater emission reductions and transformational change.

Voluntary vs. Compliance Markets: Carbon credit markets can be voluntary or compliance-based. Voluntary markets enable individuals and companies to offset emissions voluntarily, while compliance markets operate under regulatory mandates.

Innovations and Future Trends: Advancements in technology, such as blockchain and IoT, enhance transparency and accountability in carbon credit transactions. Emerging trends include nature-based solutions, circular economy projects, and blue carbon initiatives.

Conclusion: Carbon credits and project-based mechanisms offer a practical way to incentivize emission reductions and promote sustainable development. By channeling investments into projects that deliver co-benefits and contribute to global climate goals, these mechanisms play a crucial role in the transition to a low-carbon future.

Chapter 9: Carbon Market Regulation and Governance

In this chapter, we explore the scientific principles and frameworks that underpin the regulation and governance of carbon markets. These mechanisms are vital for ensuring transparency, integrity, and effectiveness in the operation of carbon markets.

Market Design and Regulatory Frameworks: Effective carbon market design requires a comprehensive regulatory framework. Regulatory bodies set rules, standards, and oversight mechanisms to ensure fair and efficient market operation.

Market Oversight and Transparency: Robust market oversight ensures the accuracy of reported emissions and the validity of carbon credits. Transparency mechanisms include regular reporting, third-party verification, and public access to information.

Accounting and Verification: Accurate accounting of emissions and reductions is essential for the credibility of carbon markets. Verification processes involve independent assessments to ensure compliance with established standards.

Linking and International Cooperation: Linking carbon markets across jurisdictions enhances market liquidity and expands emission reduction opportunities. International cooperation is crucial for harmonizing standards and ensuring equitable participation.

Case Study: European Union Emissions Trading Scheme (EU ETS): The EU ETS is the world's largest carbon market. Its regulatory framework includes the monitoring, reporting, and verification of emissions, and the establishment of a central registry for tracking allowances.

Price Stability and Market Mechanisms: Price stability mechanisms, such as price floors and ceilings, prevent extreme price fluctuations. Market mechanisms, like the Market Stability Reserve in the EU ETS, help manage supply and demand imbalances.

Carbon Leakage and Trade Measures: Carbon leakage occurs when emissions-intensive industries relocate to regions with weaker carbon regulations. Trade measures, such as border carbon adjustments, aim to prevent competitive disadvantages.

Stakeholder Engagement and Public Participation: Engaging stakeholders, including governments, businesses, and civil society, enhances market legitimacy and effectiveness. Public participation ensures diverse perspectives are considered in decision-making.

Ethics and Social Equity: Carbon markets raise ethical concerns, including the potential for environmental injustice and displacement of vulnerable communities. Ensuring social equity requires fair distribution of costs and benefits.

Market Integrity and Avoiding Fraud: Stringent enforcement measures prevent fraud, double-counting, and misrepresentation of emissions reductions. Strong penalties deter non-compliance and uphold market integrity.

Market Evolution and Future Challenges: Carbon market regulation must evolve to accommodate emerging challenges and opportunities, such as technological advancements, changing policy landscapes, and market linkages.

Safeguarding Environmental Integrity: Ensuring environmental integrity is paramount. Rigorous regulation and governance prevent "hot air" credits and ensure that genuine emissions reductions are achieved.

Conclusion: Effective carbon market regulation and governance are essential for building trust, incentivizing emission reductions, and achieving global climate goals. A robust regulatory framework ensures that carbon markets contribute to a sustainable and low-carbon future.

Chapter 10: Carbon Market Future and Prospects

In this chapter, we delve into the scientific insights that shape the future of carbon markets and their potential to drive global climate action. We explore emerging trends, technological advancements, and the role of carbon markets in achieving long-term sustainability.

Technological Innovations and Market Evolution: Advancements in monitoring technologies, data analytics, and blockchain are revolutionizing carbon market transparency, accuracy, and efficiency.

Decentralized Ledger Technology and Smart Contracts: Blockchain technology offers secure and tamper-proof record-keeping, enabling real-time tracking of emissions reductions and carbon credit transactions.

Tokenization and Fractional Ownership: Tokenizing carbon credits enhances accessibility and liquidity, allowing individuals and small investors to participate in carbon markets.

Digitalization and Satellite Imaging: Satellite data and remote sensing enable accurate measurement of forest cover, deforestation rates, and land-use changes, enhancing the accuracy of emissions accounting.

Innovations in Measurement and Verification: Advanced methodologies, such as remote sensing, IoT devices, and machine learning, improve the accuracy and cost-effectiveness of emissions measurement and verification.

Nature-Based Solutions and Blue Carbon: Nature-based solutions, including coastal and marine ecosystems, contribute to carbon sequestration and offer co-benefits for biodiversity and ecosystem services.

Carbon Removal Technologies: Emerging carbon removal technologies, such as direct air capture and enhanced mineralization, have the potential to remove carbon dioxide from the atmosphere at scale.

Enhanced Market Linkages: Increasingly interconnected carbon markets foster global collaboration, enabling the transfer of emissions reductions across borders.

Emergence of Carbon Offsets and Removal Credits: Carbon markets are exploring the integration of offsets and removal credits to incentivize investments in carbon removal projects.

Inclusion of Non-CO2 Climate Forcers: Expanding carbon markets to address non-CO2 climate forcers, such as methane and black carbon, can enhance their impact on mitigating climate change.

Market Resilience and Adaptation: Carbon markets must adapt to evolving climate risks and policy landscapes, ensuring their continued effectiveness in a changing world.

Enhanced Public and Private Sector Collaboration: Close collaboration between governments, businesses, and civil society is crucial for shaping effective carbon market policies and strategies.

Addressing Social Equity and Just Transition: Carbon markets should prioritize social equity, supporting communities and workers impacted by transition to low-carbon economies.

Youth Engagement and Climate Education: Engaging youth in carbon market discussions fosters climate literacy and empowers the next generation of climate leaders.

Conclusion: The future of carbon markets holds immense promise, driven by technological innovation, international cooperation, and ambitious climate targets. These markets are poised to play a pivotal role in accelerating the global transition to a sustainable and resilient future.

Annex A. List of verification organizations.

1. Verified Carbon Standard (VCS): Abstract: VCS is a widely recognized carbon standard that provides a rigorous framework for the validation and verification of carbon offset projects. VCS-certified projects undergo comprehensive assessments to ensure their emissions reductions are real, additional, measurable, permanent, and independently verified. The VCS standard covers various sectors, including forestry, renewable energy, and waste management.

2. Gold Standard (GS): Abstract: The Gold Standard is a premium carbon certification standard that ensures projects not only reduce emissions but also contribute to sustainable development and other environmental and social benefits. GS-certified projects adhere to strict criteria, promoting sustainable practices and local community engagement.

3. Climate Action Reserve (CAR): Abstract: CAR is a leading carbon offset registry in North America. It establishes protocols and guidelines for the development of carbon offset projects, particularly in sectors like forestry, agriculture, and waste management. CAR conducts third-party verification to confirm emissions reductions and issues carbon credits for trading.

4. American Carbon Registry (ACR): Abstract: ACR is a recognized carbon offset program in the United States. It focuses on project-based emissions reductions across various sectors and provides transparent methodologies for quantifying and verifying carbon offsets. ACR-certified projects contribute to addressing climate change and promote sustainable practices.

5. Plan Vivo Foundation: Abstract: The Plan Vivo Foundation focuses on community-based reforestation and agroforestry projects that enhance carbon sequestration while improving livelihoods for local communities. Projects adhere to Plan Vivo's standards for social and environmental co-benefits and are validated and verified by independent experts.

6. Forest Stewardship Council (FSC): Abstract: FSC is a renowned certification body for responsible forest management. While not exclusively a carbon market verification organization, FSC-certified forests contribute to carbon sequestration and sustainable land use practices. FSC's standards encompass ecological, social, and economic aspects of forest management.

7. Climate, Community & Biodiversity Alliance (CCBA): Abstract: CCBA standards focus on projects that address climate change, support local communities, and conserve biodiversity. Projects certified by CCBA provide verified emissions reductions while promoting positive impacts on people and ecosystems.

8. Det Norske Veritas (DNV): Abstract: DNV is a global assurance and risk management company that offers third-party verification services for carbon offset projects. DNV's expertise ensures that projects meet the required standards for emissions reductions and contribute to sustainable development goals.

9. Société Générale de Surveillance (SGS): Abstract: SGS is a multinational company specializing in inspection, verification, and certification services. SGS conducts independent assessments of carbon offset projects to verify emissions reductions and ensure compliance with relevant standards.

10. TÜV Rheinland: Abstract: TÜV Rheinland is an internationally recognized testing and certification organization. It provides independent verification services for carbon offset projects, evaluating the accuracy of emissions reductions and the adherence to established protocols.

Annex B. Types of Investors.

1. Financial Institutions:

o Investment Banks: Large financial institutions, such as JPMorgan Chase, Goldman Sachs, and Morgan Stanley, engage in carbon trading and provide financing for carbon offset projects.

o Asset Management Companies: Companies like BlackRock and State Street Global Advisors manage investment funds that include carbon market-related assets.

2. Renewable Energy Companies:

o Companies involved in renewable energy, such as wind, solar, and hydroelectric power, often invest in carbon markets to offset emissions from their operations and enhance their sustainability efforts.

3. Industrial Corporations:

o Energy-Intensive Industries: Companies in sectors like oil and gas, manufacturing, and chemicals may invest in carbon markets to comply with emissions regulations and manage their carbon footprints.

o Aviation and Shipping: Airlines and maritime companies invest in carbon offsets to mitigate emissions from their operations, often in compliance with international agreements like CORSIA for aviation.

4. Private Equity Firms:

o Private equity firms, such as KKR and The Carlyle Group, may invest in carbon offset projects as part of their sustainable investment strategies.

5. Carbon Funds and Traders:

o Carbon Funds: Entities like the World Bank's Carbon Finance Unit and the International Finance Corporation (IFC) manage carbon funds that invest in emission reduction projects in developing countries.

o Carbon Traders: Specialized trading companies like Redshaw Advisors and Evolution Markets facilitate carbon trading and investment.

6. Hedge Funds:

o Some hedge funds engage in carbon trading and may invest in carbon credits and offset projects.

7. Climate Finance Institutions:

o Green Climate Fund (GCF): GCF supports developing countries in their climate mitigation and adaptation efforts, including investments in carbon offset projects.

o Climate Investment Funds (CIFs): CIFs provide funding for projects that promote low-carbon development and sustainable forestry.

8. Government and International Organizations:

o National Governments: Some governments invest in carbon markets to achieve emission reduction targets and comply with international agreements.

o United Nations: UN bodies like the United Nations Framework Convention on Climate Change (UNFCCC) support carbon market development through various initiatives.

9. Environmental Non-Governmental Organizations (NGOs):

o Some environmental NGOs invest in carbon offset projects as part of their climate action initiatives.

10. Individual Investors:

o High-net-worth individuals and retail investors may invest in carbon credits through specialized investment funds or platforms.

Annex C. Main Carbon Markets.

1. European Union (EU):

o The EU operates the largest carbon market in the world, known as the European Union Emissions Trading System (EU ETS). It covers various industries and sectors across EU member states.

2. United States:

o Several states, including California and the northeastern states in the Regional Greenhouse Gas Initiative (RGGI), have established carbon trading systems. Additionally, voluntary carbon markets exist in the U.S.

3. China:

o China has launched a national carbon market, which is gradually expanding and covers sectors such as power generation.

4. Japan:

o Japan has introduced a voluntary carbon market and has been exploring options for emissions trading.

5. Canada:

o Canada has both federal and provincial carbon pricing mechanisms, including emissions trading systems in some provinces.

6. Australia:

o Australia has implemented a carbon pricing mechanism and also has voluntary carbon markets.

7. South Korea:

o South Korea operates an emissions trading system covering various sectors.

8. New Zealand:

o New Zealand has established an emissions trading scheme to regulate greenhouse gas emissions.

9. Switzerland:

o Switzerland has implemented its own emissions trading system.

10. Norway:

o Norway has a national emissions trading system covering various industries.

11. Chile:

o Chile has launched a carbon market and is actively working to expand its carbon pricing efforts.

12. Mexico:

o Mexico has introduced a voluntary carbon market and is exploring further carbon pricing mechanisms.

13. Brazil:

o Brazil has explored the establishment of carbon markets and has engaged in discussions related to emissions trading.

14. South Africa:

o South Africa has introduced a carbon tax and is considering further carbon market initiatives.

15. India:

o India is exploring options for carbon pricing and emissions trading as part of its climate mitigation efforts.

16. Singapore:

o Singapore has announced plans to implement a carbon pricing mechanism and establish a carbon trading market.

*****

Milton Keynes UK
Ingram Content Group UK Ltd.
UKHW052116010224
437019UK00006B/48